THE TAPPING STICK

D.A. Jennings

Illustrated by Dan Kane

Rob and Bonnie,

my sojourners in life through
youth's passing seasons
into adulthood.

Gratitude for all living things.
Respect for all differences.
Love for the family tree.

Under the shade
of the mahogany tree,
there laid a stick strong
and straight. Within my
hand, I felt its weight.

I knew what it would be...
a tapping stick of course.

With a smack and a whack, I tapped a mighty rock. With a thump and a bump, I tapped the ground. With a splish and a splash, I tapped the water and ripples spread.

At the base of an old birch tree remained a stick of white and gray. Within my grip, the wood began to sway.

I knew what it would be... a conducting stick of course.

With a flick of the stick, crows cawed, a sapsucker pecked, chickadees chickadee-deed, bees buzzed, and deer watched.

Walking along the road,
I spotted a wall of leaves.
Bamboo is not a tree but
it grows tall and green.
I chose a sturdy shoot and
took it to the stream.

I knew what it would be...
a fishing stick of course.

Quietly, I sat, where the rocks watched over the water. The stream flowed swiftly; the sun got hotter. A tug pulled at my stick. I reacted quick. Back and forth we fought but it was a rusty can I caught. I cast my hook back in the water.

Trash lay under the willow tree.
Its hanging boughs wept and sighed.
I picked up a stick with leaves
and held it to my side.

I knew what it would be...
a sweeping stick of course.

Geese stepped over plastic bottles.
Around paper plates, ducks waddled.
Fishing line entangled a discarded box.
A shopping bag nestled between two rocks.
All this littering was wrong. So, I swept up all
that did not belong.

One afternoon while walking, we found ourselves surrounded by dogwood trees. Cooper took off running. I wondered what he'd seen. Within his mouth, he held something long and lean.

I knew what it would be... a fetching stick of course.

I kept him guessing where the stick would go. Sometimes soaring high; other times low. With each bark, he pleaded for one more throw; neither of us wanting to go. The last toss traveled south. Proudly, he carried that stick in his mouth.

Between two rocks, I smashed
a shell from the macadamia tree.
From inside the seed's hard coat,
a buttery nut waited for me. As I
sat to eat, a branch on the ground
scraped my knee.

I knew what it would be...
a digging stick of course.

First, I dug for earthworms by the lake
but only found a three-striped garter snake.
Deep within a cave, I mined for specks of gold.
In my backyard, I buried a time capsule in a hole.
Among wildflowers, I poked around for
arrowheads. But only found the spikes
of the flowering dragonhead.

I climbed a hill close to a maple tree. The rocks on the ground were plentiful and loose. My foot slipped on a stick and I claimed it for my use.

I knew what it would be...
a helping stick of course.

A staff to walk the land.
A crutch to help me stand.
A pole for poking piles of leaves.
And a prod to get apples out of trees.

Across the ridge, towered the spruce, pine, and fir trees. All conifers, their scents came to me on a winter's breeze. Their fallen branches lay all around and many I did seize.

I knew what they would be...
building sticks of course.

Removing all the cones, I stacked them like stones. Then inch by inch, I pinched off all the needles. Fir sticks became my floor. Pine framed my window and spruce would become my door.

The fragrance of sharpened pencils
came from the red cedar trees.
The sweet, citrus-like smell reminded
me of driftwood, a long-ago gift from
the sea. The stick was gnarled and
weathered, and fit nicely in my hand.

I knew what it would be...
a writing stick of course.

A soaring seagull became my muse; the sand a blank page for words I'd choose. Incoming tides brought waves of stories to me and with the stick, I wrote until the sun touched the sea. I stood and looked around. Words covered every inch of sand. It's amazing what can be done with the proper stick in your hand.

Standing guard, at the top of the hill, is the mightiest of oak trees. Throughout our youth, it offered us sticks to do with as we pleased.

Sticks of many sizes served as swords to fight our fears. Shadows fled into the woods prodded by our spears.

But today, I claim no stick to hold
because there's something I must do...

Within our hands
we hold the future...

and I'm planting
a tree for you.

Observances Relating to Trees

Observance	Date
International Day of Forests	March 21st
Earth Hour	Last Saturday in March
Earth Day	April 22nd
Arbor Day	Last Friday in April (U.S.) varies by state & by country
World Environmental Day	June 5th
World Day to Combat Desertification & Drought	June 17th
World Rainforest Day	June 22nd
World Nature Conservation Day	June 28th
World Environmental Health Day	September 26th

Thanks to

The Creator of Nature

&

The Guardians of Nature

Arbor Day Foundation (1872)

U.S. Forest Service (1905)

National Park Service (1916)

U.S. Fish and Wildlife (1940)

Bureau of Land Management (1946)

You and Me

Special thanks to James McFarland for reviewing this book and sharing his knowledge about trees.

CPSIA information can be obtained
at www.ICGtesting.com
Printed in the USA
BVHW022001190621
609897BV00022B/185

9 781737 276104